The Oojamaflip

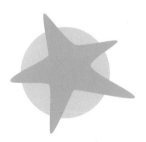

Maverick
Early Readers

'The Oojamaflip'

An original concept by Lou Treleaven

© Lou Treleaven

Illustrated by Julia Patton

Published by MAVERICK ARTS PUBLISHING LTD

Studio 3A, City Business Centre, 6 Brighton Road,

Horsham, West Sussex, RH13 5BB

© Maverick Arts Publishing Limited January 2019

+44 (0)1403 256941

A CIP catalogue record for this book is available at the British Library.

ISBN 978-1-84886-400-9

www.maverickbooks.co.uk

Turquoise

This book is rated as: Turquoise Band
The original picture book text for this story has been modified
by the author to be an early reader.

The Oojamaflip

by **Lou** Treleaven

illustrated by **Julia** Patton

Professor McQuark had a very big brain.

She loved inventing things.

She was testing her self-making bed when

– PING! She had an idea.

"I will call it an Oojamaflip," said

Professor McQuark.

She ran to her shed.

She banged, clanged, sawed and sanded.

The Oojamaflip was finished.

Professor McQuark gave it a final polish

and set off for the town's Science Fair.

But the Oojamaflip was too big to take in!

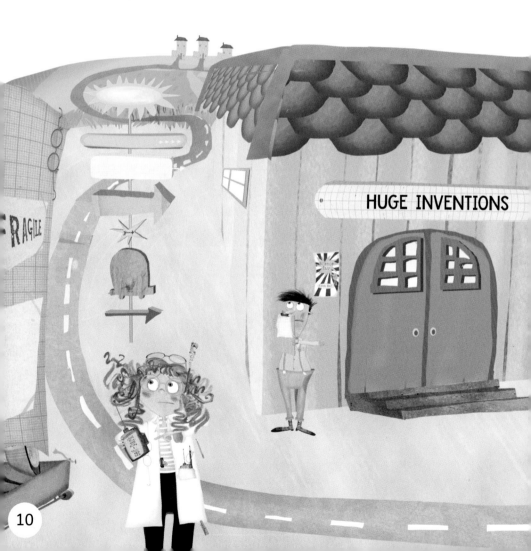

"Oh dear!" sighed Professor McQuark.
"Now the Oojamaflip won't be in
the competition."

BIG INVENTIONS

TOWN HALL

LITTLE INVENTIONS

Professor McQuark decided to have
a look round anyway.

The Science Fair was crammed with
inventions from all over the world.

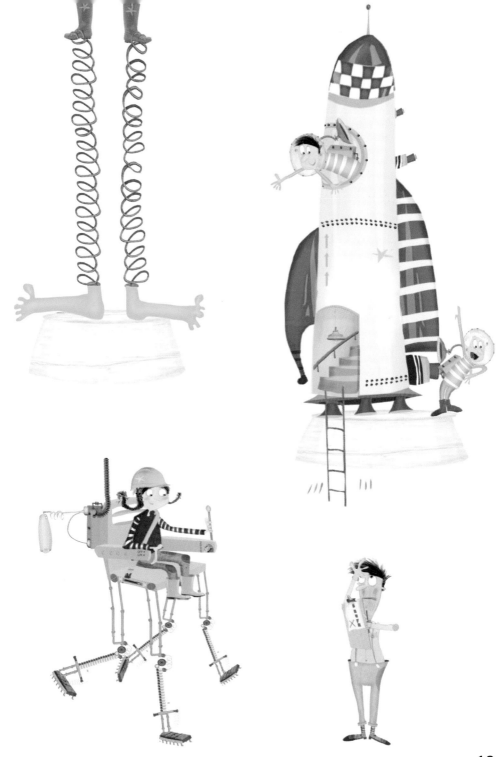

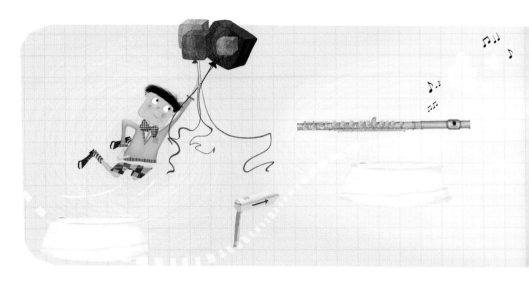

There was a man who made square

balloons, a flute that played itself...

...a stretchy alien suit, a yo-yo with

slo-mo, and even a door with a zip.

The judges looked at each invention carefully so they could decide who was going to win.

"The winner is... the square balloon maker!" said the head judge.

"But where has everyone gone?"

The judges and Professor McQuark

hurried outside, following the sounds

of laughter and shouting.

"Look what we've found!" cried the children.

The judges stared at the Oojamaflip.

They didn't know what to make of the spare deckchair on the back.

Or the doughnuts.

The grass seats were a surprise.

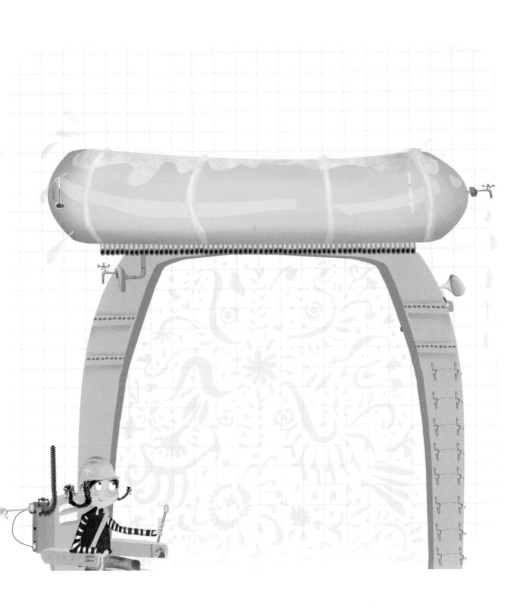

So was the paddling pool on the roof.

"It's amazing. It's fantastic!" they said.

"But what does this Oojamaflip actually do?"

"The clue is in the name," said Professor

McQuark. She pressed a button.

"It oojamaFLIPS!"

The judges decided to give the Oojamaflip

a prize too - for giving them a surprise!

Quiz

1. What does Professor McQuark love to do?
a) Invent
b) Cook
c) Knit

2. Where does Professor McQuark take the Oojamaflip?
a) To her friend's house
b) To school
c) To the Science Fair

3. Why can't Professor McQuark take the Oojamaflip inside?
a) It breaks
b) It is too big
c) It vanishes

4. What invention do the judges say is the winner of the fair?
a) The flute that played itself
b) The square balloons
c) The door with a zip

5. What does the Oojamaflip do?
a) It sets off fireworks
b) It makes balloons
c) It oojamaFLIPS

Book Bands for Guided Reading

The Institute of Education book banding system is a scale of colours that reflects the various levels of reading difficulty. The bands are assigned by taking into account the content, the language style, the layout and phonics. Word, phrase and sentence level work is also taken into consideration.

Maverick Early Readers are a bright, attractive range of books covering the pink to white bands. All of these books have been book banded for guided reading to the industry standard and edited by a leading educational consultant.

To view the whole Maverick Readers scheme, visit our website at

www.maverickearlyreaders.com

Or scan the QR code above to view our scheme instantly!

Quiz Answers: 1a, 2c, 3b, 4b, 5c